Teaching Scientific Enquiry

Contents

Introduction: *Teaching Children about scientific enquiry*

When we ask children to carry out science investigations we want them to work as independently as they can. We want them to:

- raise questions
- choose an appropriate approach
- plan what to do, choose what equipment to use
- predict what might happen
- use equipment and carry out practical work safely
- make observations and take measurements
- present evidence in tables, charts and graphs
- draw conclusions
- describe patterns and trends
- compare results to predictions, make further predictions
- explain their findings and evaluate the strength of the evidence.

This is a long list of skills; and we cannot expect children to succeed in investigations unless we have first taught them about the skills that they will need to use. However, it can be difficult finding the time to teach children skills during busy periods of investigating. We often spend much of our time simply managing what is happening. This book contains activities to help you teach the skills of investigation to lower junior pupils. None of the activities should take long to carry out but all should help you equip your pupils with the skills they need to become more independent investigators.

How to use this book: *Questions and Answers*

What will I find in the book?

There are lots of quick activities, called **Skill Activities**, presented on photocopiable worksheets. They are designed to improve children's knowledge and understanding of particular skills.

Should I do these Skill Activities instead of hands-on investigations?

The **Skill Activities** are not intended to replace hands-on investigations where children learn from first hand experience and direct observation. There can be no substitute for that. However, investigating is a complex process; children find it difficult to think about all the skills at once and often become overwhelmed. These **Skill Activities** break down the skills into small manageable units which children can learn and then apply the next time they carry out a scientific enquiry.

Which skills are taught in the book?

Nine different skills are developed through various **Skill Activities**:

- asking questions and having ideas
- deciding on an approach
- planning what to do
- choosing equipment
- presenting evidence
- drawing conclusions and describing patterns in results
- comparing results to predictions and making further predictions
- explaining evidence
- evaluating.

Other than 'Making predictions' and 'Using Equipment', which can only be tackled in the context of a scientific enquiry, all the skills are covered.

Do I need to work through the book in the order of the skills?

It is up to you to select the specific **Skill Activities** that you think your class needs to develop. If, for example, you feel that your class lacks confidence in presenting evidence, then turn to that section. You can use the **Skill Activities** in the order that suits you and your class.

When should I use the Skill Activities?

You can use them at any time but you will find it most helpful to use sheets just before your class tackles a scientific enquiry in which they will need to use that skill. You should find that they are then able to apply the skill with more confidence and independence, when doing the investigation.

How do I know that these Skill Activities will match the level of attainment in my class?

New Star Science has a **Skills Ladder** (see page 5) which describes how children make progress in the different skills as they become older. All the activities are linked to the level of demand suggested for lower junior pupils in the **Skills Ladder**.

How can we make sure that there is progression in skills through the school?

There are similar New Star Science books to help you teach the same skills at infant and upper junior levels. They also contain **Skill Activities** matched to the appropriate year groups on the **Skills Ladder**.

Can I use this book alongside any scheme of work or other published material?

The **Skill Activities** can be used alongside any scheme of work or other published material, including New Star Science and the QCA scheme of work.

What is scientific enquiry?

'Scientific enquiry' is a term that encompasses different types of practical work in science. The essential aspect of a scientific enquiry is that pupils make some decisions about how to go about the enquiry and what to make of the evidence.

There are several ways of carrying out scientific enquiries including:

Fair testing

In these enquiries you change one factor (the independent variable) measure the effect on another factor (the dependent variable) and keep other factors the same to make the test fair. For example, if testing how the temperature of the water affects the time taken for sugar to dissolve, you would change the temperature, measure the time taken to dissolve and keep the volume of water, number of stirs and amount and type of sugar the same.

Finding an association

These enquiries usually occur when you are working with animals, including humans, or in the environment. In these contexts, it is often impossible to carry out a fair test because you cannot keep all relevant factors the same. For example, if you wanted to know whether there is a relationship between the height of a person and their pulse rate, you would find it impossible to do a fair test, changing only the height of people and keeping all other factors such as weight, age group and fitness level the same. Instead you see if there is an association between height and pulse rate by measuring these things across a reasonable sample of people. In these cases you cannot link cause and effect, you can only note an association.

Classifying

In these enquiries, you arrange a variety of objects or events into sets. It is important that children decide the criteria for sorting into sets, and also pick out other features that the members of the sets have in common. For example, if classifying small invertebrates according to the number of legs, they may recognise that all those with six legs have their legs attached to the middle of their three body segments. Or if classifying materials into those attracted to a magnet and those not attracted to a magnet, they may recognise that it is only certain metals that are attracted.

Exploring

For these enquiries you make careful observations or measurements of objects or events over time. You have to decide what is worth observing or measuring, and how often the observations or measurements should be made. For example, you might study the growth of one bean plant over several weeks or you might observe how the Moon changes shape.

Problem-solving

In these enquiries you find a way to solve a specific problem. You have to design, test and adapt an object or a system. For example you might find a way to clean dirty water or to make a flashing light on top of a model Christmas tree.

The majority of science enquiries carried out in primary schools are of the fair-testing type. Likewise, the majority of the **Skill Activities** in this book focus on the skills that children need to carry out a fair test. However, the **Skill Activities** also feature some of the skills needed for other types of scientific enquiry as shown on the table opposite.

Skill Activity	Type of Scientific Enquiry
1	Fair Testing
2	Fair Testing
3	Various
4	Various
5	Fair Testing
6	Fair Testing
7	Fair Testing
8	Finding an association
9	Various
10	Exploring
11	Fair Testing
12	Exploring
13	Various
14	Fair Testing
15	Fair Testing
16	Fair Testing
17	Fair Testing
18	Fair Testing
19	Fair Testing
20	Classifying
21	Fair Testing
22	Fair Testing
23	Fair Testing
24	Fair Testing
25	Fair Testing
26	Fair Testing
27	Fair Testing

Skills Ladder

New Star Science covers all the skills used in scientific enquiry. However, it is vital that you increase the complexity and demand of these skills as pupils go through the school. New Star Science is built around the **Skills Ladder** which outlines how the skills of scientific enquiry build from year to year. This framework ensures that your pupils progress in scientific enquiry.

The **Skills Ladder** is organised under three main headings: Planning; Obtaining and presenting evidence; and Considering evidence and evaluating. The appropriate skills for each year (R to 6) are listed under these headings.

By working through the New Star Science Units, the children will naturally climb the **Skills Ladder**. Within each Unit several skills areas are covered, although there are some Units where practical work is difficult to carry out and the skills have less emphasis, such as Earth, Sun and Moon. Most New Star Science Units provide a good range of skills work, allowing flexibility, even if all the Units are not used.

All the activities in this book are linked to the level of demand suggested for lower junior pupils in the **Skills Ladder.** Most of the **Skill Activities** are pitched at National Curriculum level 3 (level C in Scotland) although a few relate to either level 2 or 4. You will find extra guidance about the level of demand in the Teacher's Notes.

New Star Science Skills Ladder

	Planning				
	Asking questions and having ideas	**Deciding an appropriate approach**	**Planning the detail of what to do**	**Predicting what might happen**	**Choosing what equipment to use**
R	Asks questions about objects and events. Tries out things when handling equipment	Tries out different approaches suggested to them.	Sometimes suggests next step in a plan.	Sometimes suggests what might happen in a specific instance in response to teacher's prompt.	Recognises that different equipment is needed for different things.
Year 1	Asks questions using a range of question stems e.g. How? What will happen if? Why? Tests ideas suggested to them.	With support identifies questions that can be answered by trying it out and those that cannot.	Suggests next step, or steps, in a plan.	Suggests what might happen in a specific instance in response to teacher's prompt.	Begins to choose appropriate equipment from a limited range with support from the teacher.
Year 2	With support, asks questions leading to scientific enquiry.	Sorts questions into those that can be answered by trying it out and those that cannot.	With support, describes the observations or measurements they need to take, spots when a plan will lead to an unfair test and recognises hazards.	With support, sometimes predicts outcomes of enquiries.	Chooses appropriate equipment from a limited range with support from the teacher.
Year 3	Sometimes asks questions leading to scientific enquiry.	Knows there are different ways of answering scientific questions.	In a fair test, identifies what to keep the same. With support plans main steps in other types of enquiry. Recognises most hazards.	Sometimes predicts outcomes to enquiries.	Selects appropriate equipment from a wider range with support from the teacher.
Year 4	Asks questions and offers own ideas for scientific enquiry.	With support knows when to answer a question by using a fair test and when evidence should be collected in other ways.	In a fair test, identifies what to keep the same and with support what to change and what to measure/observe. Plans main steps in other enquiries. Recognises hazards and support, plans how to control risks.	Predicts outcomes and sometimes suggests reasons for their prediction.	Selects appropriate equipment and with support, considers the scale and the degree of accuracy required on some measuring equipment.
Year 5	Asks questions and offers own ideas for scientific enquiry and, with support, improves question to clarify scientific purpose.	Knows when to answer a question by using a fair test and when evidence should be collected in other ways, including using secondary sources.	Sets up a fair test knowing what to change/measure/observe and what to keep the same. With support considers whether to take repeat readings. With support, plans the detail in other types of enquiry. Assesses hazards and plans how to control risks.	Predicts outcomes and, where appropriate, suggests reasons for their predictions.	Selects equipment form a wider range, including digital scales, forcemeters and computer sensors. With support, considers the scale and the degree of accuracy required on measuring equipment.
Year 6	Asks questions and offers own ideas for scientific enquiry which have a clear scientific purpose.	Identifies appropriate approach to answer a scientific question.	Sets up a fair test. Plans the detail in other types of enquiry.. With support considers whether plans will yield enough evidence for the task. Assesses hazards and plans how to control risks.	Predicts outcomes and, where appropriate sketches a graph to show the expected pattern in results. Justifies their predictions using scientific knowledge when possible.	Selects suitable equipment for a range of tasks. Takes into account the scale and the degree of accuracy required on measuring equipment.

Obtaining and presenting evidence			Considering evidence and evaluating			
Using equipment and carrying out practical work safely	**Making observations and taking measurements**	**Presenting evidence**	**Drawing conclusions and describing patterns and trends**	**Comparing results to predictions and making further predictions**	**Explaining evidence**	**Evaluating**
Follows instructions for using equipment, usually under adult supervision.	Observes simple features.	Uses drawings to present evidence and with support, uses prepared simple tables, and charts.	With support describes a simple observation made.	Recognises results that are unexpected.	Responds to prompts about cause and effect in simple situations.	With support, recognises some of the difficulties encountered.
Follows instructions for using equipment correctly and safely, sometimes working without adult support.	Makes relevant observations. with support, takes some non-standard measurements.	Uses drawings and labels to present evidence. With support, uses prepared simple tables and charts.	Describes simple observations made and with support, makes a simple comparison.	With support says whether what happened was expected in a specific instance.	With support recognises cause and effect in simple situations.	With support recognises some of the difficulties encountered.
Follows instructions for using equipment correctly and safely, usually working without adult support.	Makes relevant observations. Takes non-standard measurements. Begins to use basic equipment for measuring quantities such as length or mass, in standard units.	Uses drawings and labels to present evidence. Uses prepared tables and bar charts.	Describes what happened, making comparisons where appropriate. With support, orders results where appropriate.	Says whether what happened was expected. With support, makes further predictions from results in simple contexts.	Recognises cause and effect in most simple situations.	Recognises some of the difficulties encountered. With support, suggests how these might be avoided.
Uses basic equipment correctly and safely. Usually refers to adult when equipment fails.	Makes relevant observations. Uses standard measuring equipment for quantities such as temperature and volume.	Sometimes creates own tables and bar charts.	With support, makes a general statement about some simple patterns in results.	With support, makes further predictions from results in simple contexts.	With support, provides explanations for simple patterns in results.	Recognises the difficulties encountered. With support suggests how the enquiry might be improved.
Uses basic equipment correctly and safely. Begins to deal with equipment failures.	Makes a series of observations. Uses standard measuring equipment for measuring most quantities.	Creates own tables and bar charts. Uses a line chart with support.	Makes a general statement about simple patterns in results.	Makes further predictions from results in simple contexts.	Provides explanations for simple patterns in results.	Suggests how the enquiry might be improved. With support, recognises some of the limitations of their evidence.
Uses a wide range of equipment correctly and safely. Deals with most equipment failures independently.	Makes a series of relevant observations. With support, takes accurate readings on measuring equipment, repeating them where necessary.	Begins to select appropriate way to present evidence. Creates own bar charts and tables, including those for repeat readings Creates a line graph with support.	With support describes relationships identified, linking both factors and describing whole relationship in comparative terms.	With support makes further predictions from results and uses these to test out the suggested pattern in the relationship studied.	Sometimes relates patterns in results to scientific knowledge where appropriate.	Identifies how much to trust results. Suggests reasons why similar enquiries yield different results. With support considers the spread of repeated measurements. With support, recognises some of the limitations of their evidence.
Uses a wide range of equipment correctly and safely. Deals with equipment failures independently.	Makes a series of relevant observations. Takes accurate readings on measuring equipment, repeating them where necessary.	Selects suitable way to present evidence. Where appropriate, draws up line graph independently, except where scales involve very large or very small numbers.	Describes relationships identified, linking both factors and describing whole relationship in comparative terms.	Makes further predictions from results and uses these to test out the suggested pattern in the relationship studied.	Relates patterns in results to scientific knowledge where appropriate.	Identifies how much to trust results and justifies decision. Suggests reasons why similar enquiries yield different results. Considers the spread of repeated measurements. Recognises some of the limitations of their evidence

Curriculum Links

New Star Science Skills Ladder		England National Curriculum Key Stage 2	Wales National Curriculum Key Stage 2	Northern Ireland Curriculum Key Stage 2	Scotland 5-14 Guidelines
Planning	Asking questions and having ideas	Sc1 2a, b	The Nature of Science 1 Investigative Skills 1, 2	Planning (b)	Preparing for the task (levels B, C)
	Deciding an appropriate approach	Sc1 2a, b	Investigative Skills 3	Planning (d, e)	Preparing for the task (levels B, C)
	Planning the detail of what to do	Sc1 2c, d	Investigative Skills 3, 4	Planning (e, f)	Preparing for the task (levels B, C)
	Predicting what might happen	Sc1 2c, d	Investigative Skills 2	Planning (b)	Preparing for the task (levels B, C)
	Choosing what equipment to use	Sc1 2c, d	Investigative Skills 5	Planning (e)	Preparing for the task (levels B, C)
Obtaining and presenting evidence	Using equipment and carrying out practical work safely	Sc1 2e	Investigative Skills 6, 7	Carrying out and making (a, b, g)	Carrying out the task (levels B, C)
	Making observations and taking measurements	Sc1 2f	Investigative Skills 8, 9	Carrying out and making (d, f)	Carrying out the task (levels B, C)
	Presenting evidence	Sc1 2h	Communication in Science – all	Carrying out and making (c, h)	Carrying out the task (levels B, C)
Considering evidence and evaluating	Drawing conclusions and describing patterns and trends	Sc1 2i, j	Investigative Skills 11, 12	Interpreting and Evaluating (b, e, g)	Reviewing and reporting on the task (levels B, C)
	Comparing results to predictions and making further predictions	Sc1 2k	Investigative Skills 11	Interpreting and Evaluating (b, c, e)	Reviewing and reporting on the task (levels B, C)
	Explaining evidence	Sc1 2l	Investigative Skills 12, 13	Interpreting and Evaluating (c, g)	Reviewing and reporting on the task (levels B, C)
	Evaluating	Sc1 2m	Investigative Skills 14	Interpreting and Evaluating (f, h)	Reviewing and reporting on the task (levels B, C)

Asking questions and having ideas

Few teachers find queues of children at their desk each morning saying "I've got a good idea for a scientific enquiry". Even when we try to stimulate children into asking questions by showing them something, they may still find it difficult to come up with suitable questions.

There are probably two reasons for this. First, they can be unclear about the kind of questions that lead to scientific enquiry; and secondly they may have no strategies they can use to help them generate questions. These activities aim to help children suggest ideas for and raise their own questions.

Skill Activity 1

Purpose

To show how looking at different parts or aspects of what they are investigating can help to generate questions.

What to do

Prepare some paper spinners and put out other equipment such as scissors, paper-clips (different sizes), and different types of paper, in a central place. Get the children to look at each part of the spinner in turn and to ask themselves what they could change. Suggest that the equipment may give them some clues. Drop a spinner and ask them to think about the way you dropped it and what they could change that might affect its behaviour.

Put them in pairs or small groups and give them a time limit in which to think up as many different ideas to investigate as they can. Draw up a class list. You may find that you need to help them re-word their suggestions into a question that can be investigated e.g. 'make the wings wider' could be re-worded as 'Will changing the width of the wings affect the time the spinner takes to fall?'

Draw their attention to the way that looking at different aspects helped them to come up with ideas. Allow them a few minutes to try out some of their ideas by direct comparison (without using stopwatches).

Skill Activity 2

Purpose

To show how looking at different parts or aspects of the thing they are investigating can help to generate questions.

What to do

The first part of this activity is similar to the previous activity with paper spinners in that it asks children to consider the different aspects of dissolving in order to help them generate questions. If some pupils still find it difficult to generate questions try asking prompt questions such as 'There's a small volume of warm water in the picture; what could you change about the water?'

Asking questions and having ideas

Skill Activity 1

Name .... Date ....

Have you ever made a paper spinner?
The pictures show you a paper spinner and how to use one.

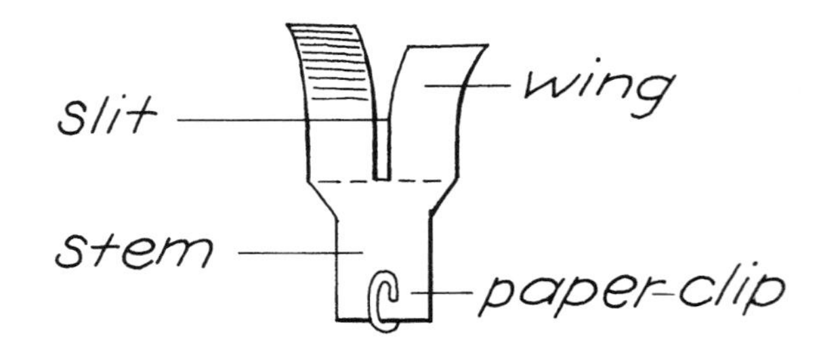

Look at each part of the spinner.
Think about which parts you could change.

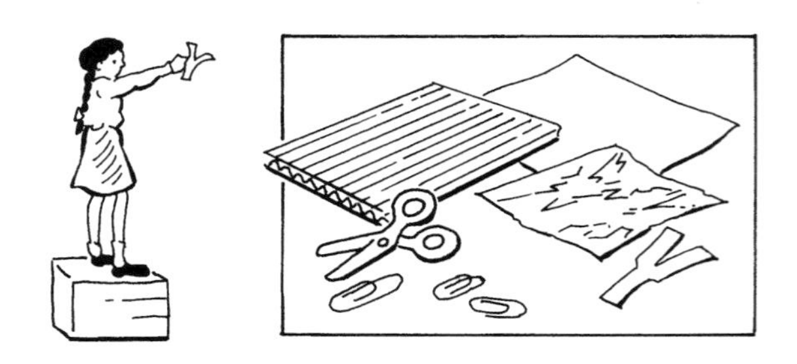

Think about how it is dropped and what you could change.

What could you change that might affect the time it takes to fall?

Write down all your ideas.

Asking questions and having ideas

Skill Activity 2

Name .... Date ....

What might make a difference to the time it takes some jelly to dissolve?

Think up some questions to investigate.

Remember to think about everything you are using in turn.

What could you change?

Questions to investigate:

Example **Will the jelly dissolve faster if I make the water hotter?**

Deciding on an approach

There are several ways of getting evidence through scientific enquiry. They include fair testing, finding an association, classifying, exploring and problem-solving (see page 4).

Before tackling a scientific question, we have to decide on a suitable approach. Lower junior pupils do not need to be able to sort all their scientific enquiries into one of these categories. However, they should become aware that there are different ways of finding out about things. Although they are likely to be very familiar with the fair test, they should know that not every science question can be tackled in this way.

They should also recognise that some scientific questions that cannot be answered by doing practical work in the classroom and where secondary evidence will be needed. These two **Skill Activities** should help pupils realise that there are other ways to find out about things other than using a fair test.

Skill Activity 3

Purpose

To know when to answer a question by using a fair test and when evidence should be collected in other ways.

What to do

Ask the children to look at the different scientific questions. Remind them that a fair test is when you change something and find out the effect it has on something else, whilst keeping all other things the same. Illustrate the structure of the fair test by getting them to think about an example such as timing how long sugar takes to dissolve in different temperatures of water. Here you change the temperature of the water, note the effect it has on the time taken to dissolve and keep other things, (e.g. amount of sugar, number of stirs and volume of water) the same.

Get them to sort the questions into those that can be tackled through the fair test and those that cannot. Questions A, D and G can be answered through the fair test. The others cannot. Discuss their responses.

Skill Activity 4

Purpose

To know when to answer a question by using a fair test and when evidence should be collected in other ways.

What to do

Ask the children to look at the questions about snails. Discuss the various ways of finding out answers to questions. Get them to sort the questions, working in pairs and have a class discussion about their responses. If children suggest looking things up in a book or CD-ROMs or asking an expert, get them to tell you how they think the authors of CD-ROMs and books, or experts, get their information. See if they can suggest how the scientists got their evidence. Ask them to make up some more questions to add to their lists.

Deciding on an appropriate approach

Skill Activity 3

Name .... *Date* ....

Some questions can be answered using a fair test.
Some need to be answered in other ways.
Here are some scientific questions.

A Which material mops up the most water?

B Do fish have ribs?

C What is the shape of my shadow?

D If I put the ramp at different heights will it make a difference to how far the car travels?

E Which materials are attracted to a magnet?

F How can I separate sand and water?

G How tall will my plants grow if I give them different amounts of water?

Sort the questions into two groups. Write the letter in the correct circle.

Can answer using a fair test.

Can not answer using a fair test.

Deciding an appropriate approach

Skill Activity 4

Name .... Date ....

Here are some questions about snails.

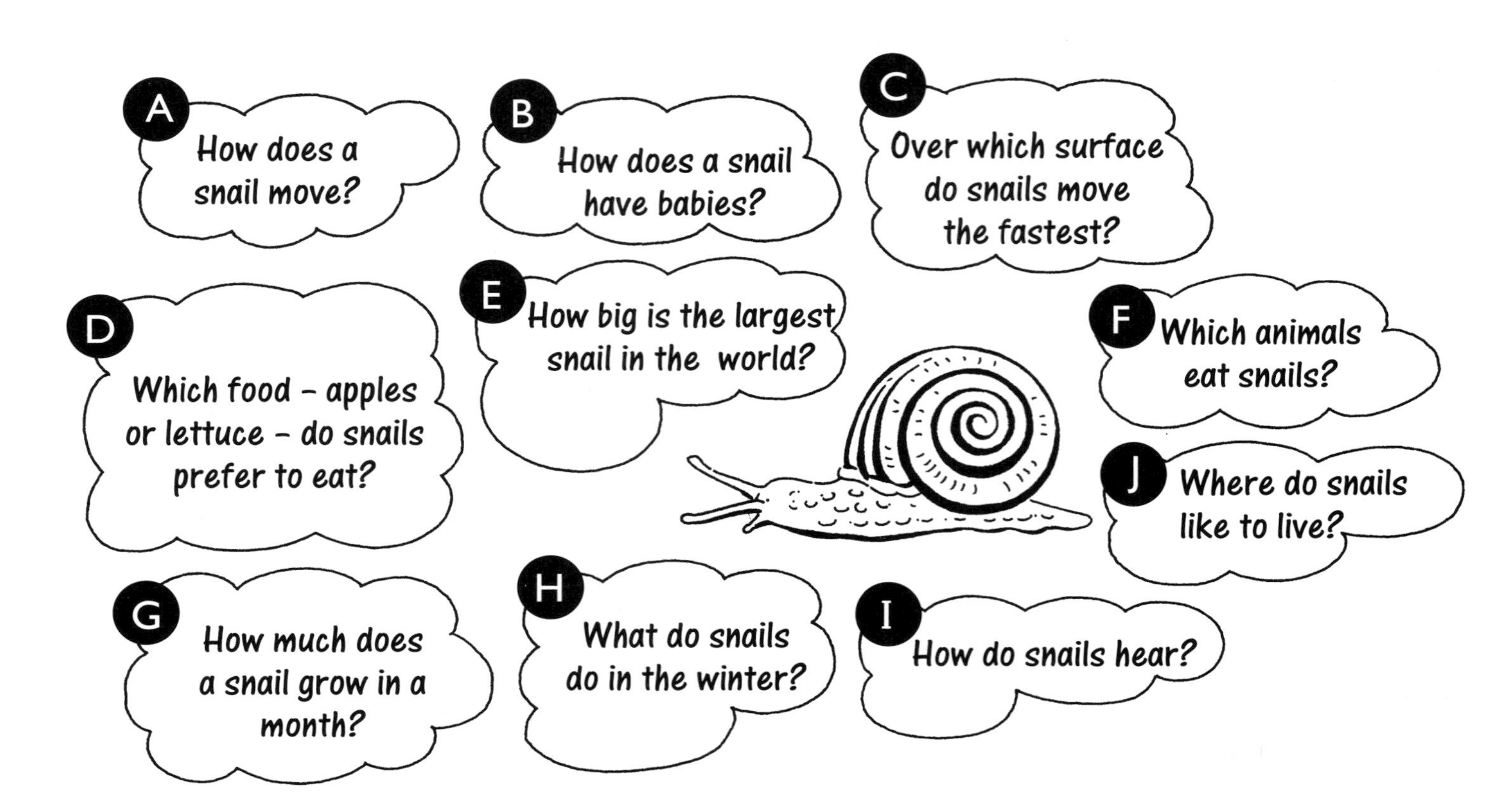

There are different ways of finding out the answers to these questions (A – J). Decide how you would find out the answers and write the letters in the correct box or boxes.

Observe and/or measure	Look in a book or on a CD-ROM or ask an expert
Carry out a survey	Carry out a fair test

Planning what to do

When lower junior children are planning what to do they need to take several planning decisions. If they are carrying out a fair test, they need to decide how to make the test fair. When children carry out a fair test, they need to know that they must only change one thing at a time. If they change more than one thing, they will not be able to tell what was causing the effect. For example, if you drop parachutes of different sizes and materials, and find out that some fall more slowly than others, you will be unable to say whether it is the size or the material (or both) that is affecting the rate of descent. **Skill Activities 5, 6** and **7** are related to the planning of fair tests.

If children are finding an association, such as whether there is a link between the circumference of a head and the height of a person, they need to decide how many people to include in their sample. **Skill Activity 8** asks pupils to begin to consider the size of the sample that they need in order to see a trend.

There will also be many scientific enquiries where children take some risks. Often, as adults, we tell them what to do to be safe. Whilst we must always remain in control of any practical work, it is important for children themselves to recognise risks and how to control them. **Skill Activities 9** and **10** raise safety issues with pupils.

If we want children to take planning decisions, we need to teach them how to take those decisions. These activities should help you to do that.

Skill Activity 5

Purpose

To know that in a 'fair test' we only change one factor, observe or measure the effect, whilst keeping other factors the same.

What to do

Have two or three different balls, two or three different surfaces and some metre rulers to hand. If they have not met this approach before, carry out Ranjit's investigation in front of them, asking them to say what is changing. Ask them to complete the other planning boards independently. Point out that in each test only one thing is changed.

Skill Activity 6

Purpose

To distinguish between a fair and an unfair test.

What to do

This activity looks at fair testing in three different contexts. Make sure the children read the captions as well as looking at the pictures so that they know what is changing in each example. The answers are:

Example	Is it a fair test?	Reason
Parachutes	Yes	Only the size of the parachute has been changed. The shape and material of the canopy and the mass on the bottom have been kept the same.
Candles	No	Two things have been changed – the size of the jar and the height of the candle.
Grass	No	Two things have been changed – the type of soil and the amount of light.

Skill Activity 7

Purpose

To know how to set up a fair test.

What to do

This activity demands more understanding than the previous activities, as the children must work out what is being changed and which other factors should be kept the same before selecting the appropriate buggies. The buggies they should choose are A, C and E. These are the same in every respect other than the size of the sail.

Skill Activity 8

Purpose

To know that a large sample gives better evidence towards a trend than a small sample.

What to do

Carry out the activity and discuss their responses. Set up a situation where someone with long legs (e.g. a non-sporty adult) jumps less far than someone with short legs (e.g. a sporty child). This may help them to realise that we cannot rely on evidence from just one or two examples, and that the larger the sample the more we can trust our results. Ask them to consider if Jan and Leo would get a more reliable answer to their question if they did their test with all 30 children in the class, or even with several classes of children.

Skill Activity 9

Purpose

To recognise hazards and suggest how to control risks.

What to do

Many activities in science (and technology) put children at risk. Most situations can be tackled safely if we take suitable action. In this activity, some children are shown taking unnecessary risks. Ask your pupils to suggest what these children could do to stay safe and to complete four science safety rules in their own words.

Skill Activity 10

Purpose

To recognise hazards and suggest how to control risks.

What to do

In this activity, children are asked to devise an electrical safety poster. This is a familiar activity; but the approach is 'here's what to do if you are foolish'. Children enjoy the chance to describe some thoughtless, and potentially lethal, activities like cutting a cable with a hedge cutter. The human body is not a particularly good conductor of electricity; but it conducts electricity far better when wet. The well-known saying 'Water and electricity don't mix' is a little misleading, as an electric current will generally flow more easily through wet things. 'Don't mix water and electricity if you want to stay safe' might be a better way of expressing things.

Planning what to do

Skill Activity 5

Name .... *Date* ....

Three children wanted to find out how to make balls bounce higher or lower. They each had a different idea. They started to write their plans. Fill in the blanks.

Ranjit

Ranjit's planning poster

I will change: ______________

I will measure: how high the ball bounces

I will keep these things the same:

the height I drop it from	the type of ball

Joanne

Joanne's planning poster

I will change: the type of ball

I will measure: how high the ball bounces

I will keep these things the same:

Kim

Kim's planning poster

I will change: ______________

I will measure: how high the ball bounces

I will keep these things the same:

Planning what to do

Skill Activity 6

Name .... *Date* ....

Here are some pictures of tests that some children carried out.
Work out if they were fair tests.

Here are our parachutes.
We'll drop them from the same height.
The strings are the same length.
We'll time how long they take to fall.

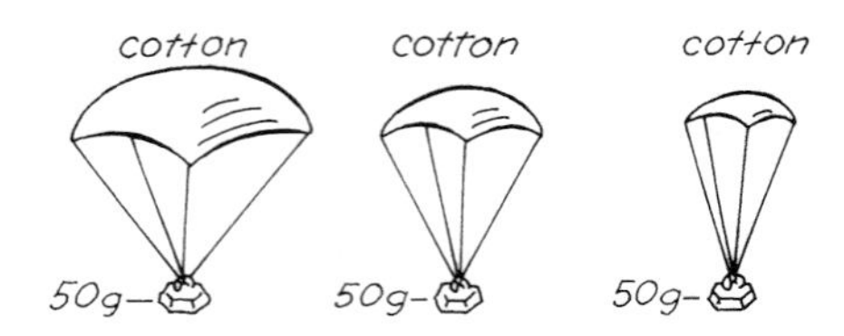

Is this a fair test? ________ Why? ____

____

We're testing how long candles stay alight in different sized jars. We'll light the candles at the same time. We'll put the jars over them at the same time. We'll time how long they take to go out.

Is this a fair test? ________ Why? ____

____

We're growing grass seed in different soils. We'll give each pot the same amount of water each day. We'll measure how tall the grass grows.

Is this a fair test? ________ Why? ____

____

Name .... Date ....

Hakan and Louise let different buggies roll down a slope.
They measured how far they went using a tape measure.

I wonder what would happen if our buggies had different sized sails.

Let's do an investigation. We must make sure we do a fair test.

Here are some different buggies:

B

C

D

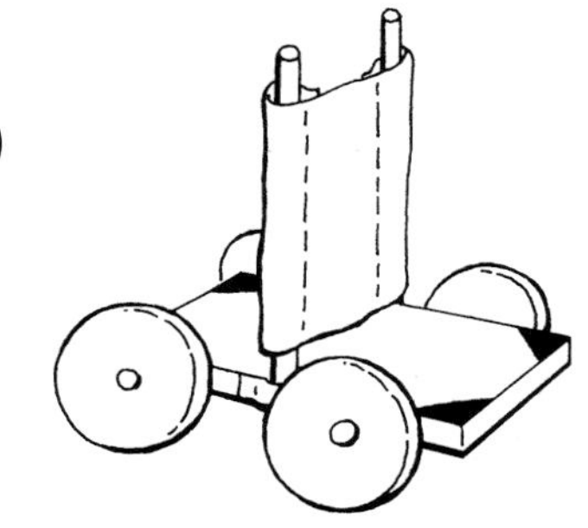

E

F

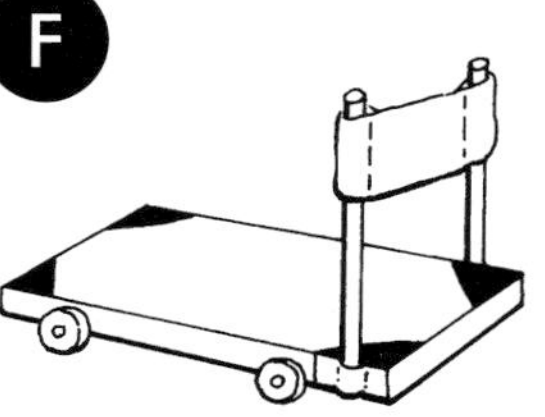

Which three buggies should the children use to test out their idea?
Write the letters.

Say why you chose these buggies.

Planning what to do

Skill Activity 8

Name .... Date ....

Jan and Leo wanted to find out if children with longer legs jump further than children with shorter legs. This is what they planned to do:

I will ask the tallest child and the shortest child in the class to do a jump. I will see who jumps further.

I will ask six children in my group to do a jump. I will measure how far they go. I will order them from longest to shortest jump. Next I will measure their legs. I will order them from longest to shortest legs. I will compare the order for jumps with the order for leg length.

Whose plan will give more useful results, Jan's plan or Leo's plan? ________________

Explain your answer:

Planning what to do

Skill Activity 9

Name .... *Date* ....

Look at the picture. Fill in the table.

	What happens next?	**What should they do?**
The girl with the kettle		
The boy with the lighthouse		
The girl with the candle		
The boy with the knife		

Write four safety rules for science. Start each one with the word 'always' .

Always ____

Always ____

Always ____

Always ____

Name .... Date ....

Paul drew his own electricity poster. He wrote:

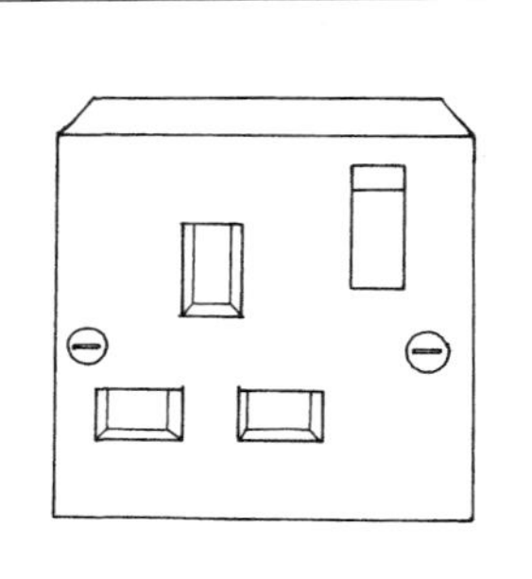

Ingredients for death

One silly kid

Water

Electricity socket

Explain what he meant:

____

____

____

Make your own electrical safety poster to put up at home. Make it for one of these places. There are some words to help you.

Kitchen

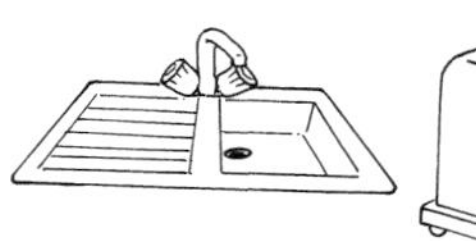

Sink

Toaster

Kettle

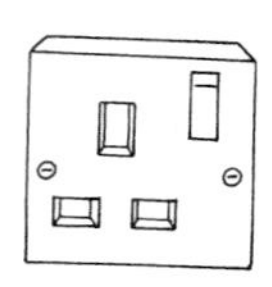

Socket

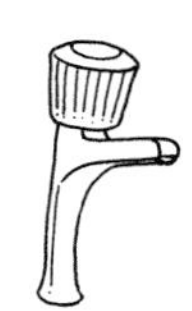

Tap

Bathroom

Radio

Shower

Fire

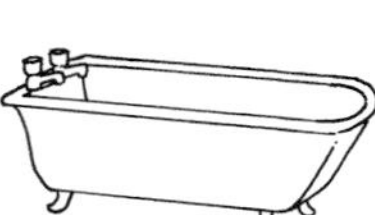

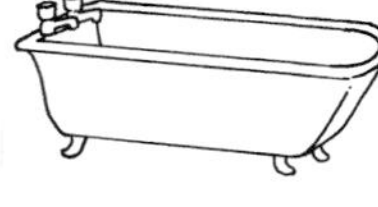

Bath

Shed

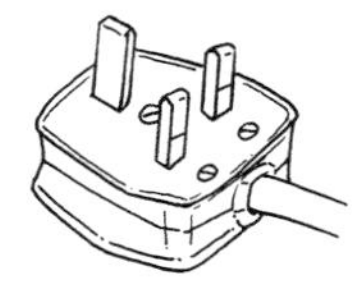

Plug

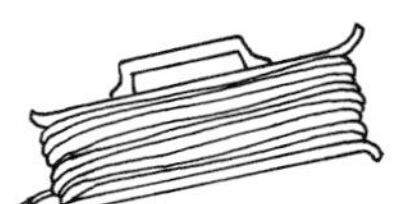

Cable

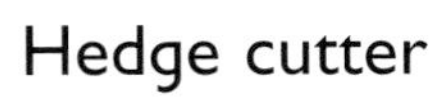

Hedge cutter

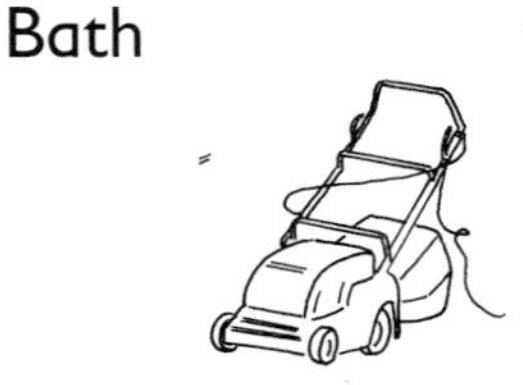

Electric mower

Garage

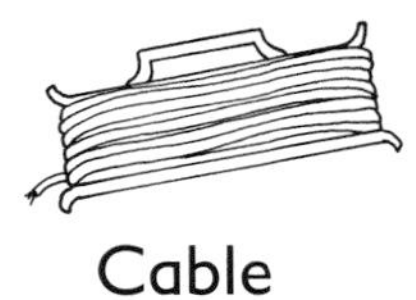

Cable

Socket

Electric drill

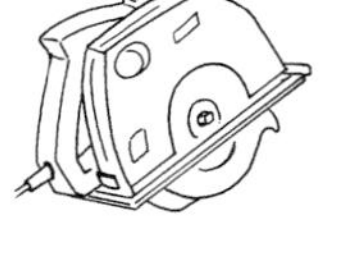

Circular saw

Choosing equipment

When considering which equipment to choose to use in their investigation, children must first decide what type of equipment is necessary, for example they may decide that they need an instrument to measure length.

Next they should consider what is an appropriate degree of accuracy. Suppose the children are doing two different investigations; finding out how far away they have to walk across the playground before they can no longer hear different sounds, and seeing how much cress plants grow in different conditions. Although they need to measure length in both cases, they will need to choose quite different equipment - a trundle-wheel to measure in metres and a ruler to measure in millimetres respectively.

We should not expect children to know how to choose equipment unless they have been taught how to use it. Many of the measuring skills they need are similar to those used in mathematics, such as the skills needed to measure length, mass, capacity, volume and time. They may therefore already be skilled in these areas but it is often worth reminding them how to use measuring equipment before they tackle an investigation. **Skill Activities 12** and **13** help children learn how to use a thermometer, as this is less likely to be part of their mathematics programme of work.

Skill Activity 11

Purpose

To decide what equipment to use in a scientific enquiry.

What to do

Before tackling this activity, make sure the children know what the investigation is about. If they are not familiar with light and temperature sensors, you may also need to explain briefly how these work. They should choose three items of equipment: the 30 cm ruler, the timer and either the thermometer or the temperature sensor.

Skill Activity 12

Purpose

To learn how to use a thermometer.

What to do

Get out as many thermometers as you can - one between two is ideal. Let the children try using the thermometers to measure the temperature of warm water. Let two or three groups of pupils put their thermometers in the same water and allow them to take temperatures in whatever way they want. It is likely that they will record different temperatures. Discuss some of the possible reasons for the different readings, bringing out the points shown on the activity sheet.

Give the children the activity sheet. They should note the following mistakes:

1. The child has lifted up the thermometer and not kept it in the water.
2. The child has not left the thermometer in the water for long enough.
3. The child does not have their eye level with the thermometer when taking the reading.

Skill Activity 13

Purpose

To learn how to use a thermometer taking account of different scales.

What to do

This sheet gives extra practice in taking readings from two different scales. Encourage the children to work out what each division on the scale represents before they read the temperatures. When they tackle the second half of the sheet, ask them to work in pairs. This way one pupil can work out the temperature that has been drawn in by their partner.

Choosing equipment

Skill Activity 11

Name .... Date ....

Kevin and Surinder were testing materials to see which kept water the warmest. They wrapped each can of warm water in different materials. They measured how hot the water was in each can after 25 minutes.

Choose the measuring equipment they could use from this list. Tick the boxes.

- [ ] 30 cm ruler
- [ ] metre rule
- [ ] force meter
- [ ] timer/stopclock
- [ ] thermometer
- [ ] measuring cylinder
- [ ] light sensor
- [ ] temperature sensor

Finish the table below.

Measuring equipment	**How would it be used?**
Example 30 cm ruler	They would use it to make sure the bits of material were the same size.

Choosing equipment

Skill Activity 12

Name .... Date ....

These children want to find out the temperature of the water in the beaker.
They are using a thermometer. Each one is doing something wrong.
Write down what you think they are doing wrong.

Lenny is wrong because:

Amy is wrong because:

Ben is wrong because:

Choosing equipment

Skill Activity 13

Name .... *Date* ....

What do these thermometers read?
Watch out! They do not all have the same scales.

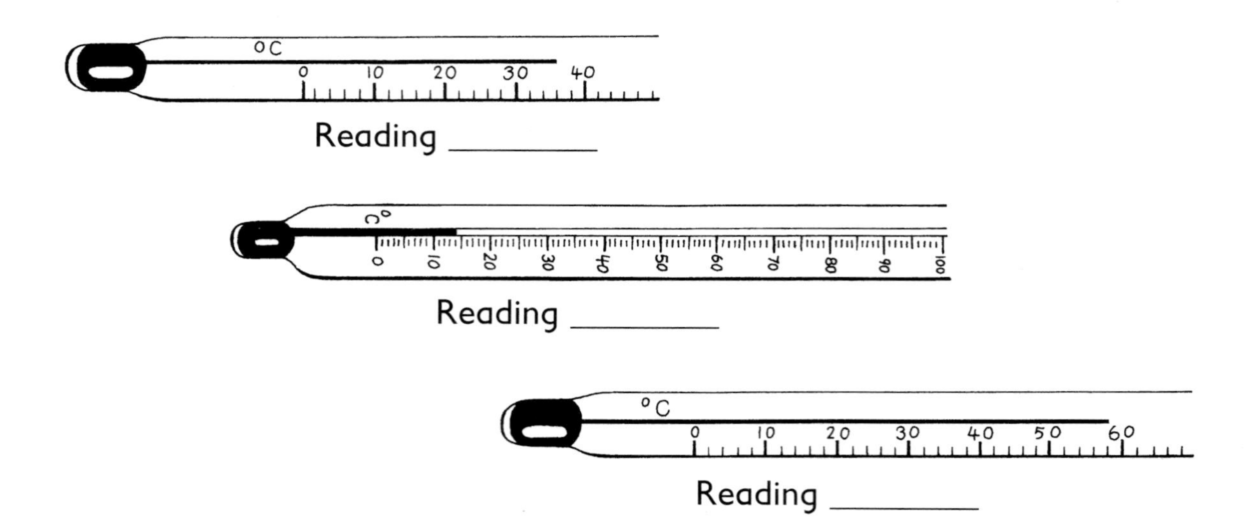

Draw some different temperatures on these thermometers by shading in the central column. Write down the readings.

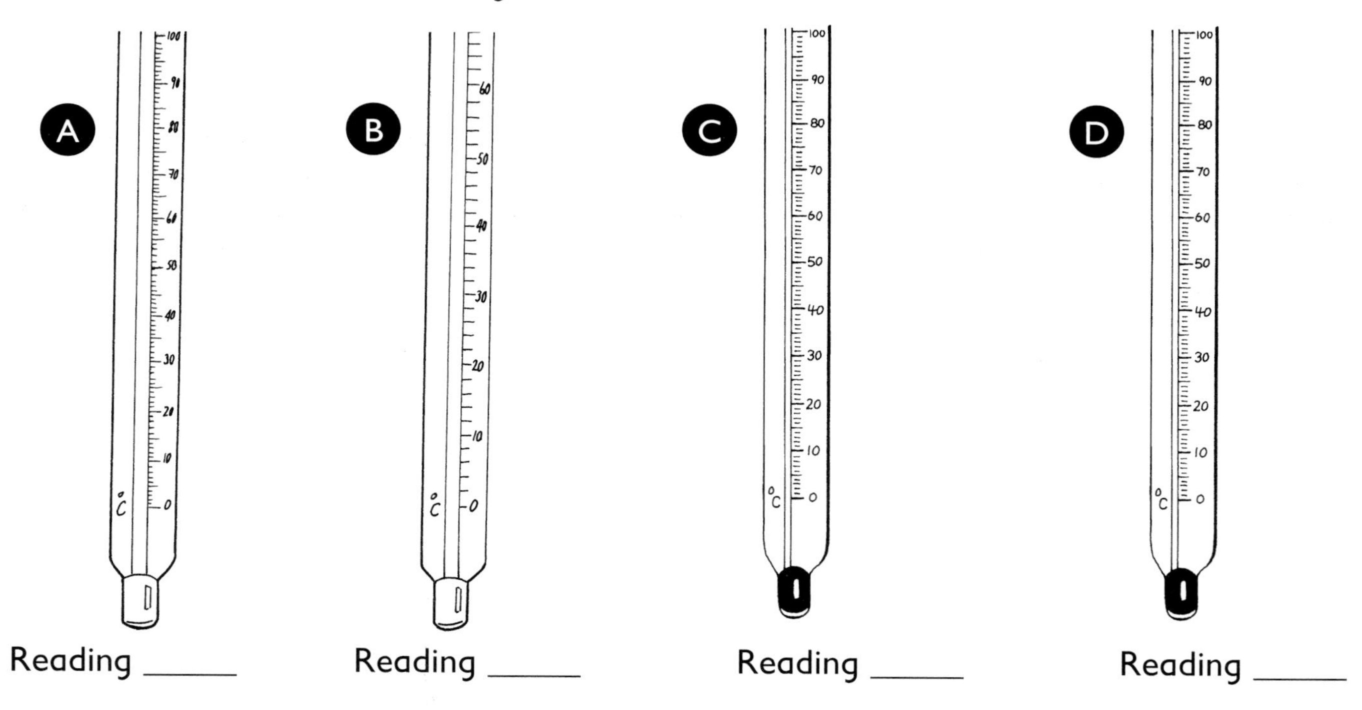

Presenting the evidence

This section helps children learn how to construct tables and bar charts in fair tests. In fair tests, you can give children strategies for presenting evidence that applies to all examples. It is not so easy to do this for other types of scientific enquiry. When children present their evidence in other types of enquiry, it is important to give them time to think about the best way of displaying their results. This will rarely be through written text alone.

We present evidence in different ways – in tables, bar charts and line graphs. In fair tests, whether you will be able to draw a table, bar chart or line graph, depends on whether 'what you changed' and 'what you measured' are expressed in words or numbers. The table below shows how this works.

Lower junior children usually only use tables and bar charts. If their enquiry leads to a line graph, you will need to offer support, for example by tackling the drawing of the line graph as a class activity.

Quite often children find technical aspects difficult, such as knowing what headings to put at the top of a table or on the axes of a bar chart. The skill activity sheets deal with these technical aspects. **Skill Activities 14, 15** and **16** help children learn how to construct a simple two column table. **Skill Activities 17, 18** and **19** help children learn how to construct a bar chart.

What you change	**What you measure**	**Type of graph or chart**
Words	Words	Table
Numbers	Words	Table
Words	Numbers	Bar Chart
Numbers	Numbers	Line Graph

Skill Activity 14

Purpose

To know how to put headings on a 2-column table.

What to do

Read through the first section with the children making sure that they realise the connection between the headings on the table and 'what we changed' and 'what we measured'. Point out that they only have to complete the headings and not the rest of the table in the other examples on the sheet.

Skill Activity 15

Purpose

To know how to construct a 2-column table.

What to do

In this activity, the children have to use information about two different investigations to help them complete the accompanying table. For each example, they need to work out what was changed and what was measured (or observed) before writing in their headings. They then need to make sure that the correct things go in each column.

Skill Activity 16

Purpose

To know how to construct a 2-column table.

What to do

Ask the children to look at the table and tell them that it has been incorrectly drawn up and that they have to spot the errors. Make sure that they understand what is going on in the investigation and tell them to study the pictures carefully.

There are five mistakes:

1 The heading on the right should say 'How much water came through (in five minutes)'.
2 Peat and 44 ml are in the wrong columns.
3 The result for Clay should be 23 ml not 36 ml.
4 Garden soil was omitted (and Sand was written twice).
5 If Garden soil replaces sand, 23 ml should be changed to 36 ml.

Skill Activity 17

Purpose

To know how to draw up a bar chart from a table.

What to do

Work through the example with the children making sure that they take in all five points.

- The heading in the left-hand column (what we change) goes to the horizontal axis on the bar chart.
- The things listed in the left-hand column (things we are testing) go on the horizontal axis on the bar chart.
- The heading in the right-hand column (what we measure) goes to the vertical axis on the bar chart.
- The scale on the vertical axis must go beyond the largest number in the right-hand column.
- We should leave spaces between the bars on our bar charts.

You may also like to carry out a class demonstration where all the information in the table is written on separate sticky notes or pieces of paper attached with Blu-tack. You can then invite children to come up and transfer the various stickers from the table onto a prepared set of axes on a large class bar chart. You can also cut out bars or columns to the correct height and stick these on the chart too. It is a good idea to consolidate these techniques by asking children to complete **Skill Activity 18**.

Skill Activity 18

Purpose

To know how to draw up a bar chart from a table.

What to do

Make sure the children know what the investigation is about, i.e. seeing how far different liquids went up strips of paper in three minutes. Ask them to complete the bar chart.

Skill Activity 19

Purpose

To know how to draw up a bar chart from a table.

What to do

Make sure the children know what the investigation is about. Ask them to spot the mistakes on the bar chart. They should notice the following:

1 The last label on the horizontal axis should say 'Star' not 'Triangle'.
2 The vertical axis should be labelled 'How far it went in cm'.
3 The vertical axis should be numbered beyond the highest reading i.e. 63 cm.
4 There should be spaces between the bars.
5 The column for the 'Triangle' is wrong. It should read 28 cm.

Name .... Date ....

Read these plans for investigations.
Write in headings for each table.

We will drop different balls and see how high they bounce. We are changing the type of ball. We are measuring the height of the bounce.

We want to find out which liquid; water, oil or honey, goes fastest down a slope. We are changing the type of liquid. We are measuring the time it takes to run down the slope.

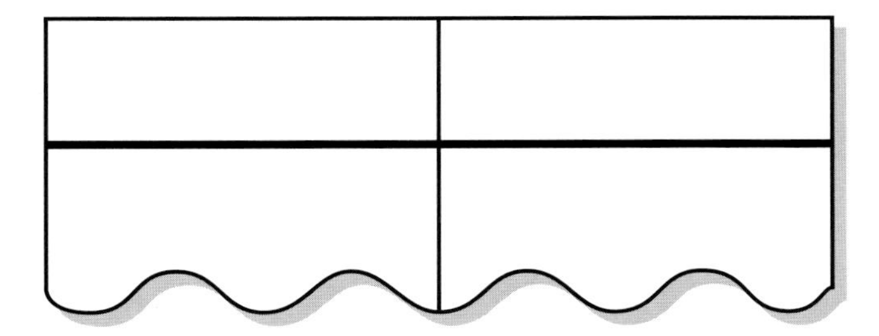

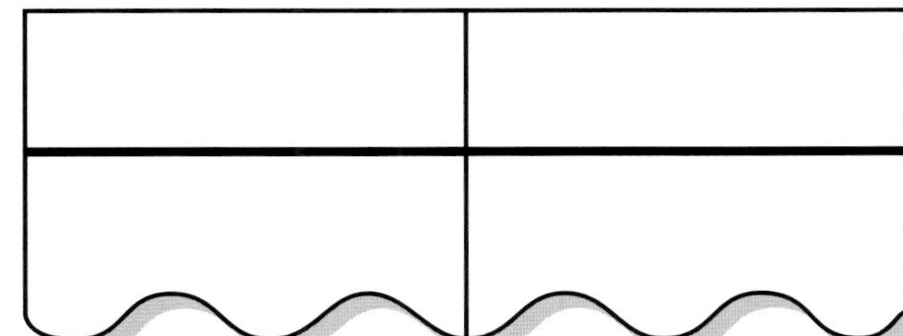

We are going to hang different weights on an elastic band. We will measure how much the band stretches.

We are going to find out how many paper-clips different kinds of magnets will pick up.

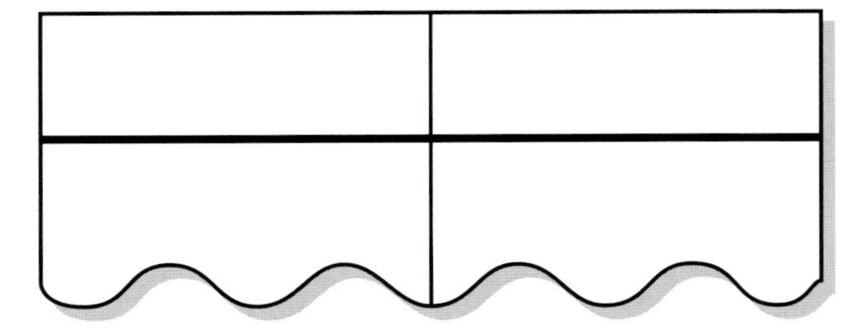

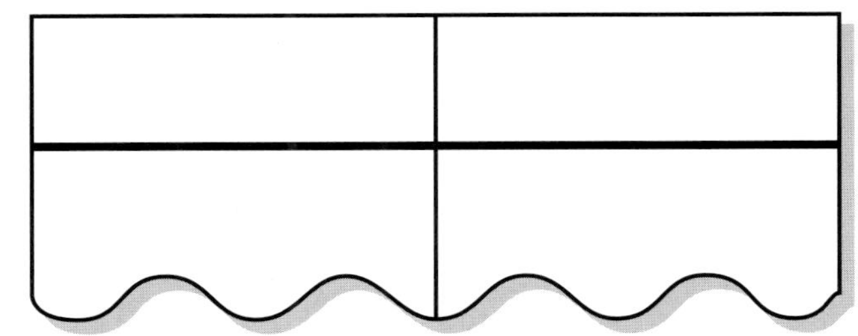

Name .... Date ....

Two groups of children are talking about what happened when they carried out their investigations. Complete the table that would go with each investigation.

We put three different batteries in the same electric circuit. We wanted to see what would happen to the brightness of the bulb. When we used a 1·5 V battery the light was very dim. When we used a 3 V battery it was quite bright; but when we used a 4·5 V battery it was very bright. We always used the same type of bulb.

	Brightness of the bulb

We found out how far a toy car, released down a ramp, would go on different surfaces. First of all we tried it on a piece of carpet and it went 38 cm; then we did it on the tiles and it went 62 cm; next we did it on some lino and it went a long way. It went 86 cm before stopping. Last of all we tried the car on some coconut matting. It only went 18 cm.

Presenting the evidence

Skill Activity 16

Name .... Date ....

Some children carried out an investigation. They poured 80 ml water onto four different soils. They found out how much water went through each soil in 5 minutes.

These pictures show what happened after 5 minutes.

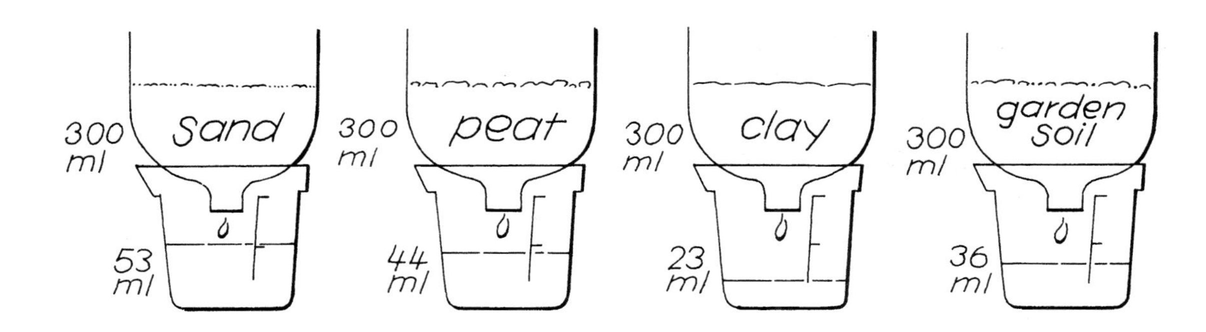

This is a table of their results. The children made several mistakes in their table. Write in bubbles on the table to say what they got wrong.

Amount of soil	How much water they poured on
Sand	53 ml
Peat	44 ml
Clay	36 ml
Sand	23 ml

Example

This is the wrong heading. It should say...

Name .... Date ....

This diagram shows you how to put results from a table onto a bar chart.

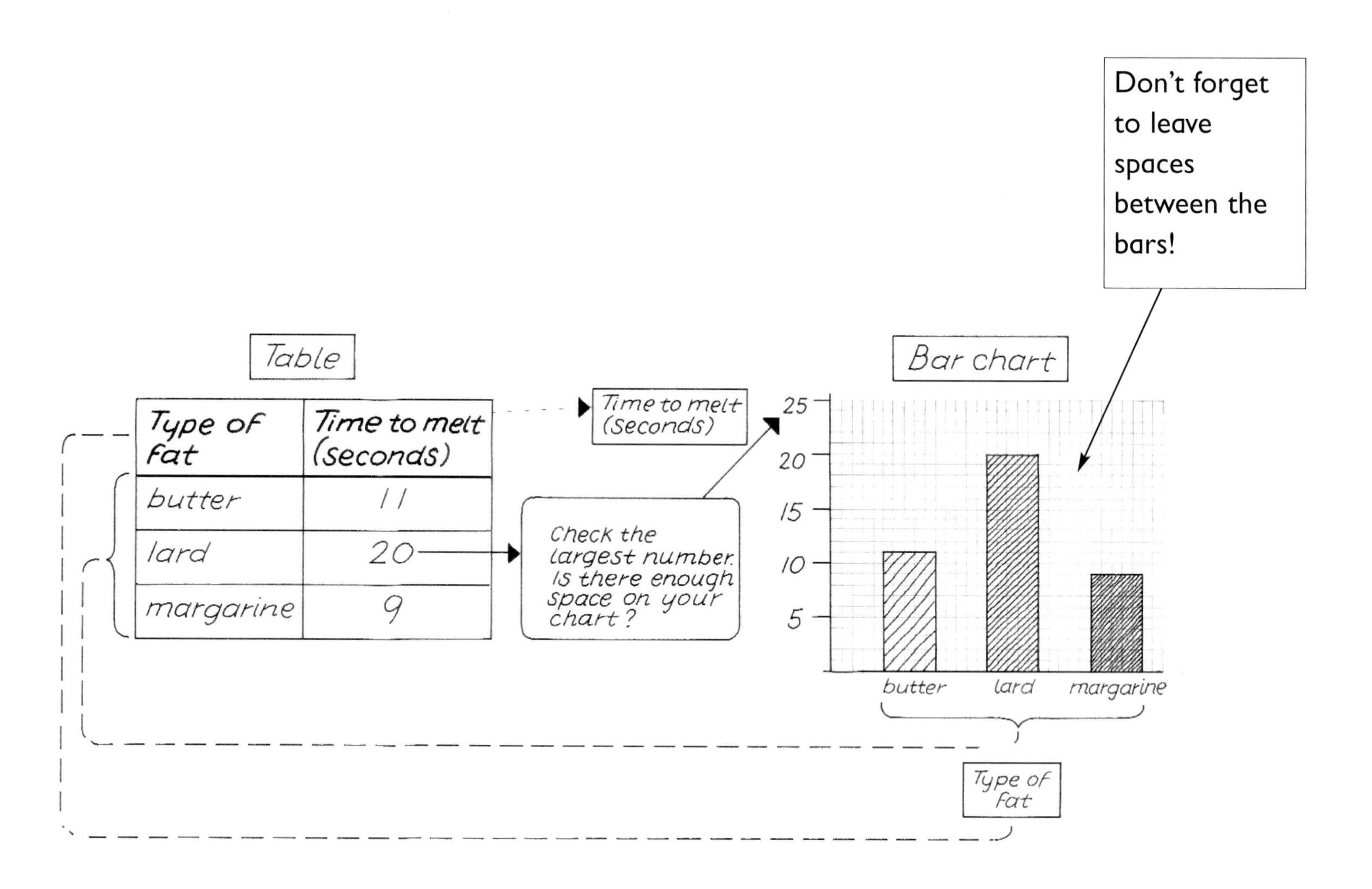

Type of fat	Time to melt (seconds)
butter	11
lard	20
margarine	9

Presenting the evidence

Skill Activity 18

Name .... *Date* ....

Some children carried out an investigation. They dangled strips of kitchen paper in different liquids and watched each strip soak up liquid. They recorded how high each liquid went in three minutes. Here is their table of results:

Type of liquid	How high the liquid went in 3 minutes (cm)
Oil	3
Ketchup	2
Water	7
Squash	6

Finish the bar chart.

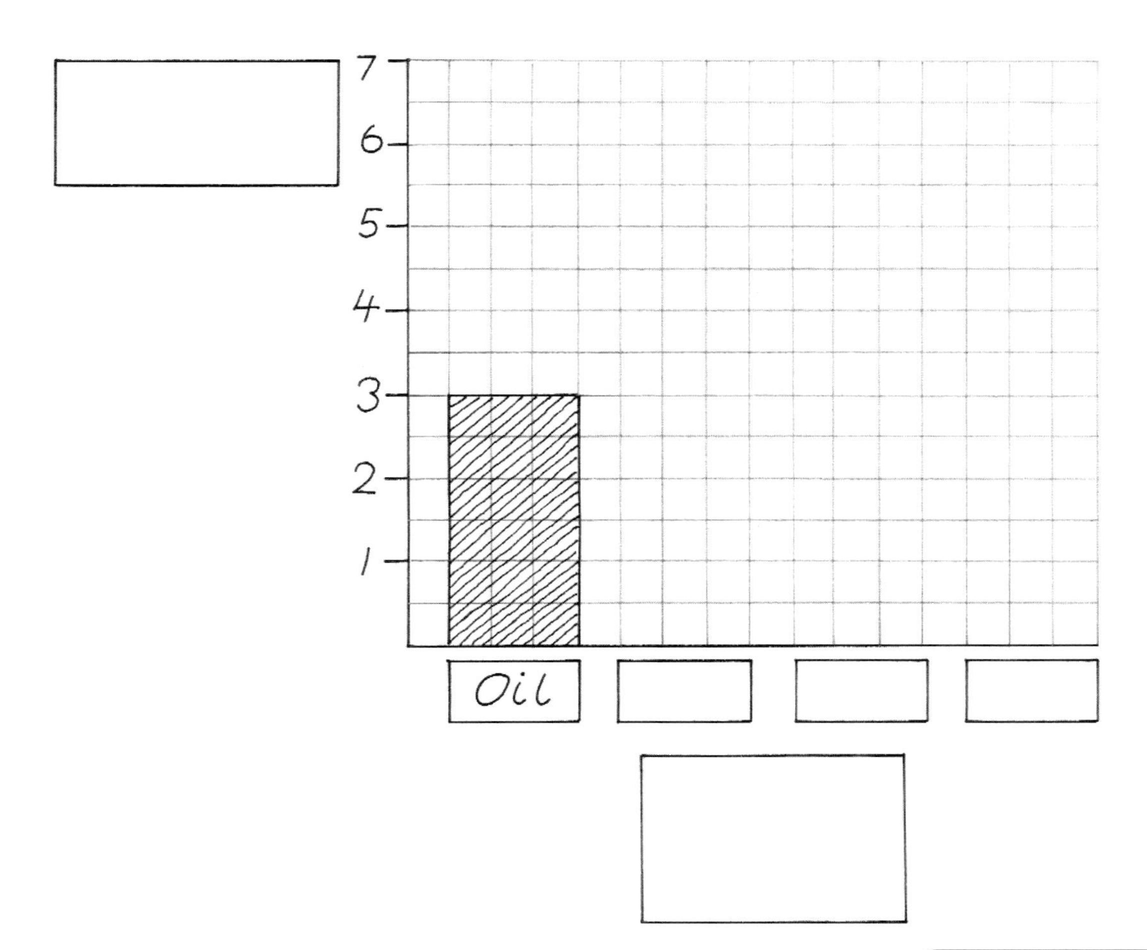

Presenting the evidence

Skill Activity 19

Name .... Date ....

Robert and Ramon tested a boat with four different shaped sails. Using a motor fan, they found out how far the boat went along a gutter of water in 10 seconds.

Here is their table of results:

Shape of sail	How far the boat travelled (cm)
Triangle	28
Rectangle	60
Circle	35
Star	31

This is their bar chart. They made five mistakes.
Write in bubbles around their bar chart to say what they have got wrong.

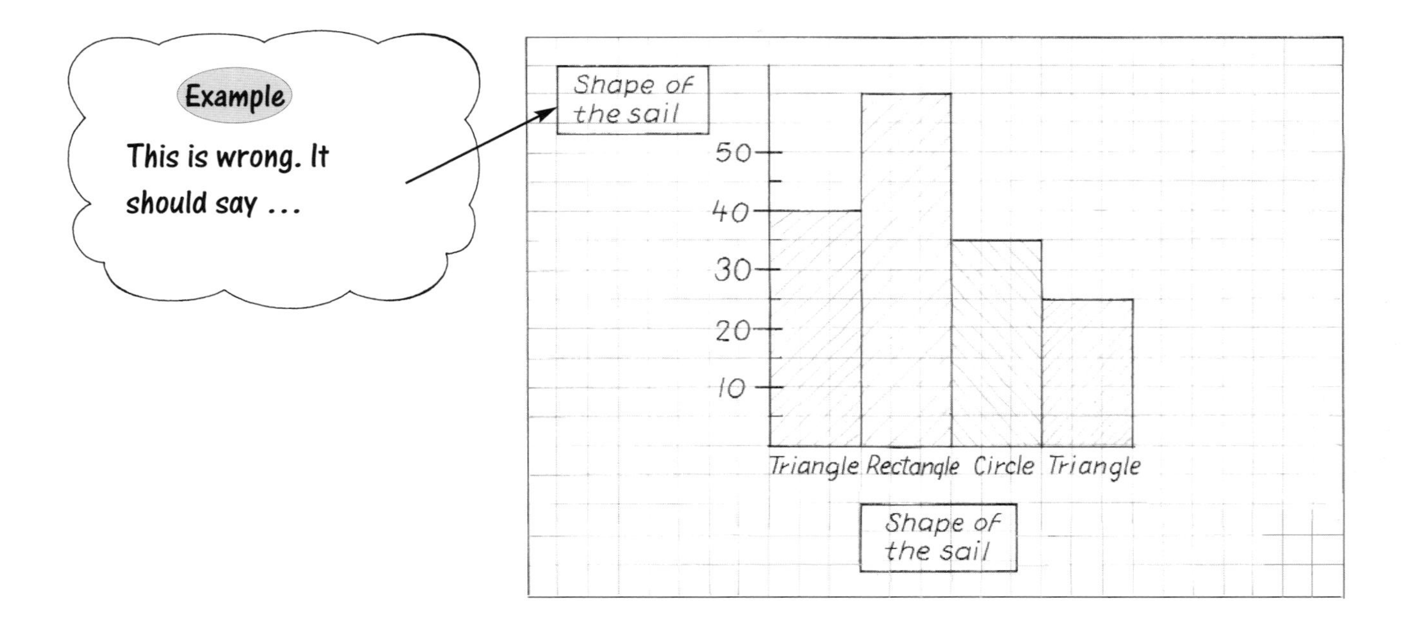

Drawing conclusions and describing patterns in results

When we ask children to draw a conclusion, we want them to sum up what their evidence tells them in a short clear statement. Their statement must match the evidence and answer their initial question or prediction. It is important that children should not make sweeping claims in their conclusions when they only have a limited amount of evidence. We also want to encourage children to make statements about the pattern in all their results, and not just about the one that 'was best'.

If children have drawn a bar chart, they should recognise that the point of drawing charts and graphs is to enable them to see patterns and trends more easily so that they can draw their conclusions. Encourage the children to say as much as possible about their bar charts, for example comparing the sizes of columns, rather than giving just one comment such as 'This one was best.' It can help them to see patterns and trends in bar charts if the columns are drawn in order of size.

Skill Activity 20

Purpose

To draw conclusions that match the evidence.

What to do

The purpose of this activity is to help pupils match conclusions to the evidence presented. It is vital to recognise the difference between a good conclusion in scientific enquiry that matches the evidence and a statement that is true in scientific terms but which does not match the evidence. In this example, whilst it is true that all metals are good conductors of electricity, the evidence only shows the results for three different metals. It is therefore impossible to draw the conclusion **from this evidence alone**, that all metals conduct electricity. The answers are as follows:

	Definitely true	Might be true	Not true
All metals conduct electricity		✔	
Only silvery metals conduct electricity			✔
We tested three different types of metal and they all conducted electricity	✔		
All these metals conduct electricity; steel, copper, gold, iron and aluminium		✔	

Skill Activity 21

Purpose

To draw conclusions that match the evidence.

What to do

This is a similar activity to **Skill Activity 20**. It asks pupils to distinguish between true and false statements using the evidence presented. Statements 1, 3, 6 are true. The others do not match the evidence presented.

Note: These results are quite likely to occur as lino often has a non-stick surface, a sort of gluey layer, which stops things sliding across it so easily.

Skill Activity 22

Purpose

To draw a conclusion describing the whole pattern in results.

What to do

This activity asks children to select the best description of results and say why it is best. It requires children to think about what makes a good conclusion. When we ask children to draw a conclusion or say what they found out they will often only give answers based on one result, rather than the whole pattern. They can also make ambiguous statements. This activity should help them to recognise that we must draw conclusions that are clear and unambiguous and which describe the whole pattern.

Allow pupils to talk in pairs or small groups before writing their answer. It is vital to discuss their responses so you can then bring out the following points.

Statement	Comment
The biggest piece was best.	Doesn't say what they mean by 'best'. Only refers to biggest piece.
The pieces of towel soaked up different amounts of water.	Does not tell you that the pieces of towel were different sizes. No reference to the pattern in the results.
The smallest one soaked up hardly any water. The biggest piece soaked up lots of water.	Only refers to two extreme results – the smallest and biggest pieces. Gives you no information about the other two sizes and the amount of water they soaked up.
The bigger the piece of towel, the more water it soaked up.	Describes the whole pattern clearly. The best description of results.

Drawing conclusions and describing patterns in results

Skill Activity 20

Name .... *Date* ....

Dipak, Paul, Jasmine and Julie sorted which materials were good conductors of electricity and which were not. They tried putting different materials in an electric circuit to see if the bulb lit.

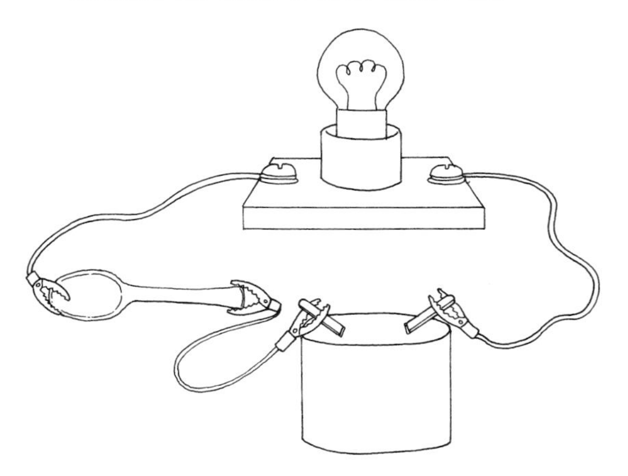

This is their table of results.

Object	Material	What happened to bulb	Good conductor (✔ or ✘)
spoon	steel	lit	✔
ruler	plastic	not lit	✘
wire	copper	lit	✔
rag	cotton	not lit	✘
kitchen towel	paper	not lit	✘
paper-clip	steel	lit	✔
piece of foil	aluminium	lit	✔

They wrote these sentences to describe their results. Put a tick in one box for each sentence. Remember, they can only use the results from their experiment.

	Definitely true	Might be true	Not true
Dipak: All metals conduct electricity.	☐	☐	☐
Paul: Only silver metals conduct electricity.	☐	☐	☐
Jasmine: We tested three different types of metal and they all conducted electricity.	☐	☐	☐
Julie: All these metals conduct electricity: steel, copper, gold, iron and aluminium.	☐	☐	☐

Drawing conclusions and describing patterns in results

Skill Activity 21

Name .... Date ....

Some children did an investigation into floor coverings. They found out how high they could tilt a board covered in different surfaces before a wooden block started to move down the board. They used more blocks to tilt the board.

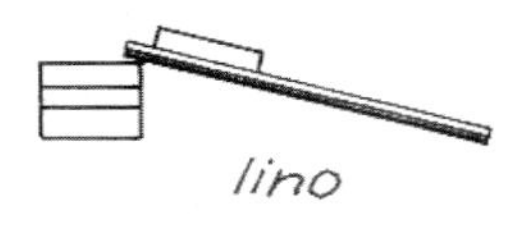

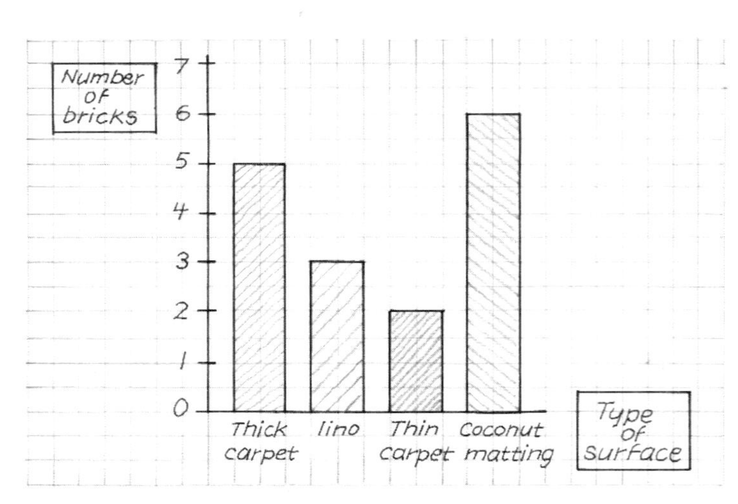

Here is their bar chart.

Ask your teacher for a separate piece of squared paper. Draw their bar chart again so the columns go from smallest to largest.

Here are some things that children said. Put a tick ✓ by the true statements. Put a cross ✗ by the false statements.

1 *We had to tilt all the surfaces more than 1 block high.* ☐

2 *We tilted the coconut matting 3 blocks higher than the thin carpet.* ☐

3 *The roughest surface was tilted the most.* ☐

4 *The smoothest surface was tilted the least.* ☐

5 *The rougher the surface the greater the tilt.* ☐

6 *For most surfaces, the rougher the surface the higher you have to tilt the board, but the lino doesn't fit this pattern.* ☐

Drawing conclusions and describing patterns in results

Skill Activity 22

Name .... Date ....

Some children cut up a towel into different sized pieces. They found out how much water each piece of towel could soak up.

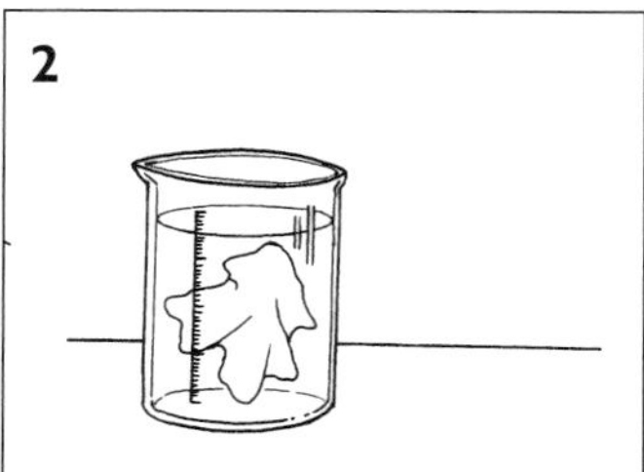

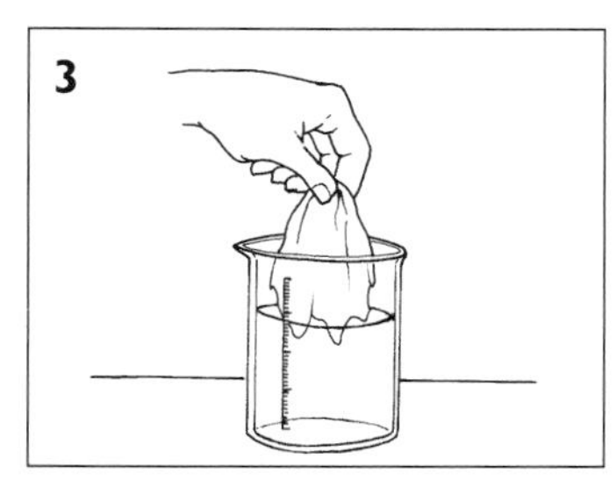

Here are their results.

Size of towel	How much water it soaked up in ml
Very small	15
Small	20
Medium	32
Big	41

Their teacher asked them to describe their results. This is what they said.

The biggest piece was wet.

Liz

The pieces of towel soaked up different amounts of water.

Raj

The bigger the piece of towel, the more water it soaked up.

Laura

The smallest one soaked up hardly any water. The biggest one soaked up lots of water.

Steve

Which one had the best description of their results? Explain your answer.

Comparing results to predictions and making further predictions

Once a scientific enquiry is completed, we often refer back to our original prediction to see whether it was correct. Also, if we have drawn a bar chart or line graph and have identified the general pattern, we can make predictions about things that we have not tested. For example we can say 'I now know that this ball bounces 23 cm on concrete and 10 cm on thick carpet and I think the pattern is the harder the surface the higher the bounce. So, I think it will bounce about 14 cm high on thin carpet'. If you ask children to make this type of prediction (sometimes referred to as interpolating and extrapolating), it is always worth following up with the question: 'That's interesting - How did you work that out?'. Usually you will find that this leads to an explanation based on their knowledge and understanding.

It is important that children realise that any prediction they make will always be tentative. We can never predict with total certainty; there will always be an element of doubt - a margin of error.

Skill Activity 23

Purpose

To compare results to predictions made.

What to do

Let the children read through the first part of the sheet. Make sure that they know which liquids are coloured and which are fizzy. Ask them to use the bar chart to check the predictions. They should record that prediction F is correct whilst predictions A, B, C, D and E are incorrect.

Skill Activity 24

Purpose

To make predictions based on evidence displayed in a bar chart.

What to do

Allow the children to read through the first part of the sheet. Make sure they realise where the two new elastic bands fit in with the ones already tested. Ask them to complete the rest of the sheet. Encourage them to tell you the general pattern that helps them make their predictions i.e. 'the thinner the band the more it stretches' or 'the thicker the band the shorter the stretch'.

Skill Activity 25

Purpose

To make predictions based on evidence displayed in a bar chart and to know that such predictions will always be tentative.

What to do

Read through the description of the investigation and discuss the bar chart and what it tells us. Also ask the children to describe the three new surfaces - the thin carpet, the sponge and the wood. Offer them a sample statement such as 'It will bounce to exactly 10 cm on the sponge' and ask them to discuss in pairs how likely this statement is to be correct. Pull their comments together and help them to realise that it is unlikely to bounce to 'exactly' any height and that it would be more likely to bounce lower, rather than higher, on the thick carpet. Ask them to complete the sheet, ticking only one box at the end of each line. Discuss their grading of the comments and their reasons.

They should record the following:

1 Very unlikely to be right.

2 Very likely to be right.

3 Quite likely to be right (although the range given is fairly narrow).

4 Unlikely to be right.

Comparing results to predictions and making further predictions

Skill Activity 23

Name .... *Date* ....

A group of children grew some grass seeds. They 'watered' them with different liquids. Before they did their investigation, they made some predictions:

A I think the grass given cold tea will grow tallest.

B I think it will grow taller in the fizzy liquids.

C The grass will not grow so well in coloured liquids.

D I think the grass will grow in all the liquids except the oil.

E Milk is good for us. I think it will be good for plants too. The grass will grow tallest in milk.

F The grass will not grow at all in vinegar, oil or milk.

After 10 days they measured the grass plants. Here is the bar chart.

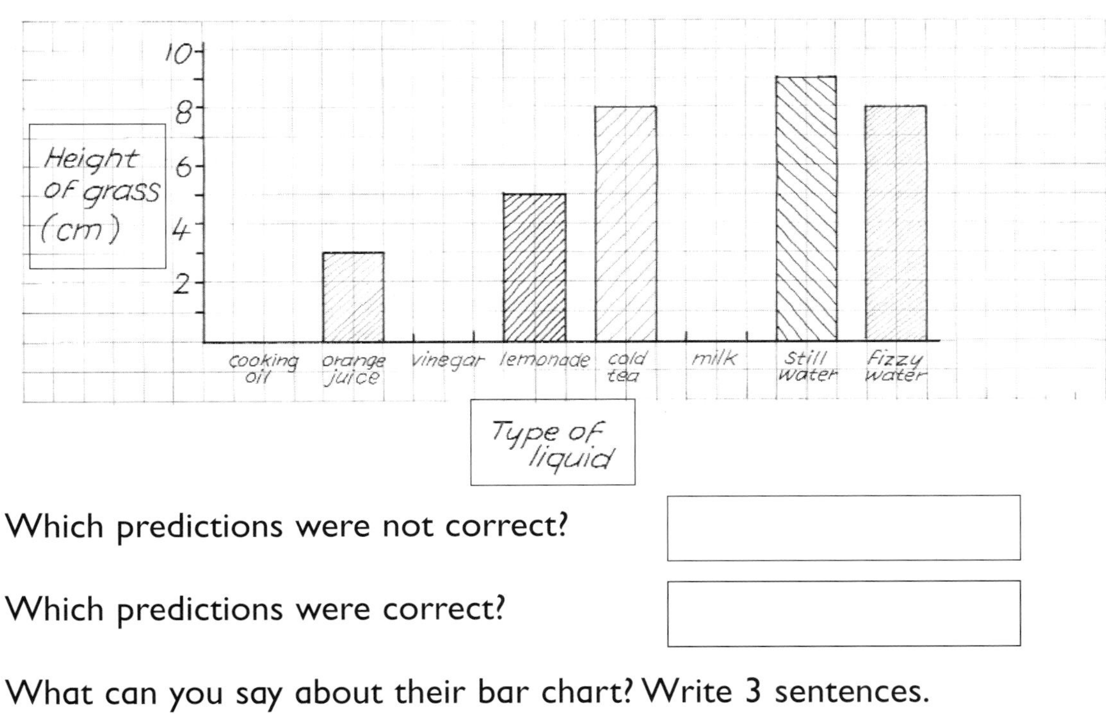

Which predictions were not correct?

Which predictions were correct?

What can you say about their bar chart? Write 3 sentences.

1 ______________________________

2 ______________________________

3 ______________________________

Comparing results to predictions and making further predictions

Skill Activity 24

Name .... Date ....

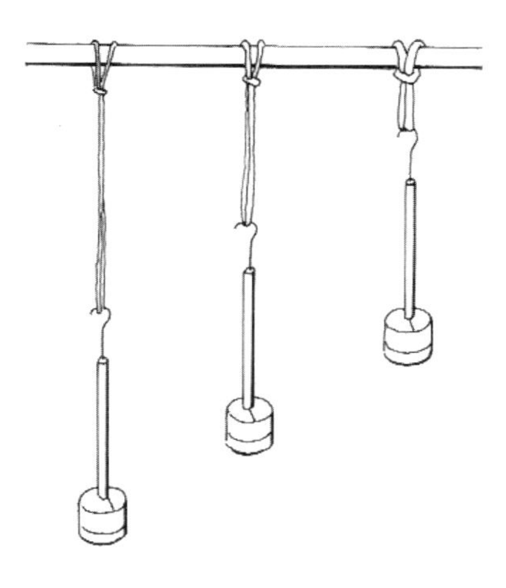

Jonathan and James carried out an investigation with elastic bands. They hung 100 g masses from different elastic bands and measured how much they stretched.

This is their bar chart.

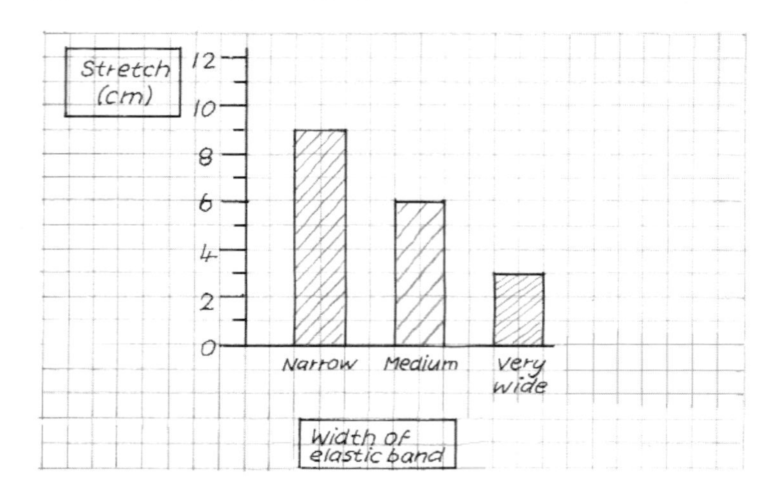

They found two more elastic bands of the same length.
One was **very** narrow and one was wide (between medium and very wide).
Use the bar chart to help you complete these sentences.
I think the very narrow elastic band will stretch to about _________ cm.
I think the wide elastic band will stretch to about _________ cm.

Write down how you worked out what to predict.

Comparing results to predictions and making further predictions

Skill Activity 25

Name .... Date ....

Jasmin and Michelle dropped the same ball from the same height onto different surfaces. They measured how high it bounced each time.

This is their bar chart.

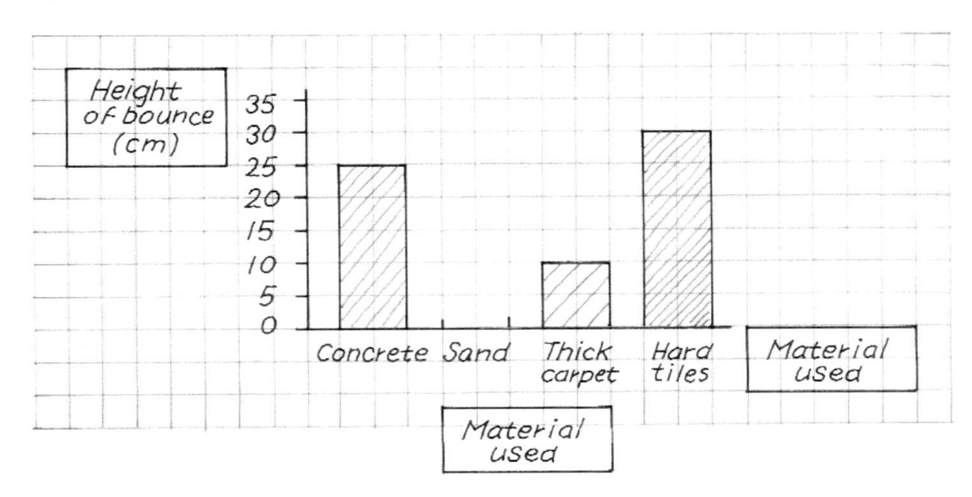

They tried to predict how high the same ball, dropped from the same height, might bounce on these three new surfaces.

	Very likely to be right	Quite likely to be right	Unlikely to be right	Very unlikely to be right
The ball will bounce exactly 15 cm on the thin carpet.	☐	☐	☐	☐
It should bounce under 10 cm on the sponge.	☐	☐	☐	☐
When we drop it on the wood it will bounce between 19 and 21 cm.	☐	☐	☐	☐
It will bounce 40 cm on the wood.	☐	☐	☐	☐

Explaining the evidence

Once we have described the evidence well in a good conclusion and either compared it with our initial prediction or made further predictions, we usually try to offer an explanation for the evidence. It can often be quite difficult to help children know what a good explanation looks like. Children also often confuse an explanation with the description of results that they give when drawing a conclusion. It can help to tell them that an explanation usually follows the word 'because' or says why something happened. **Skill Activity 26** introduces lower junior pupils to what is needed in a good explanation.

Skill Activity 26

Purpose

To know how to explain evidence.

What to do

Ask pupils read through the first part of the sheet and make sure they understand the context. Emphasise that these pupils have already described their results well by saying 'the rougher the surface, the more force you need to make the brick move', and that their teacher has asked them to give an explanation of their results. Ask them to match the explanations to the teacher's comments by linking them with lines.

The correct pairings of the pupil's explanations to the teacher's comments are:

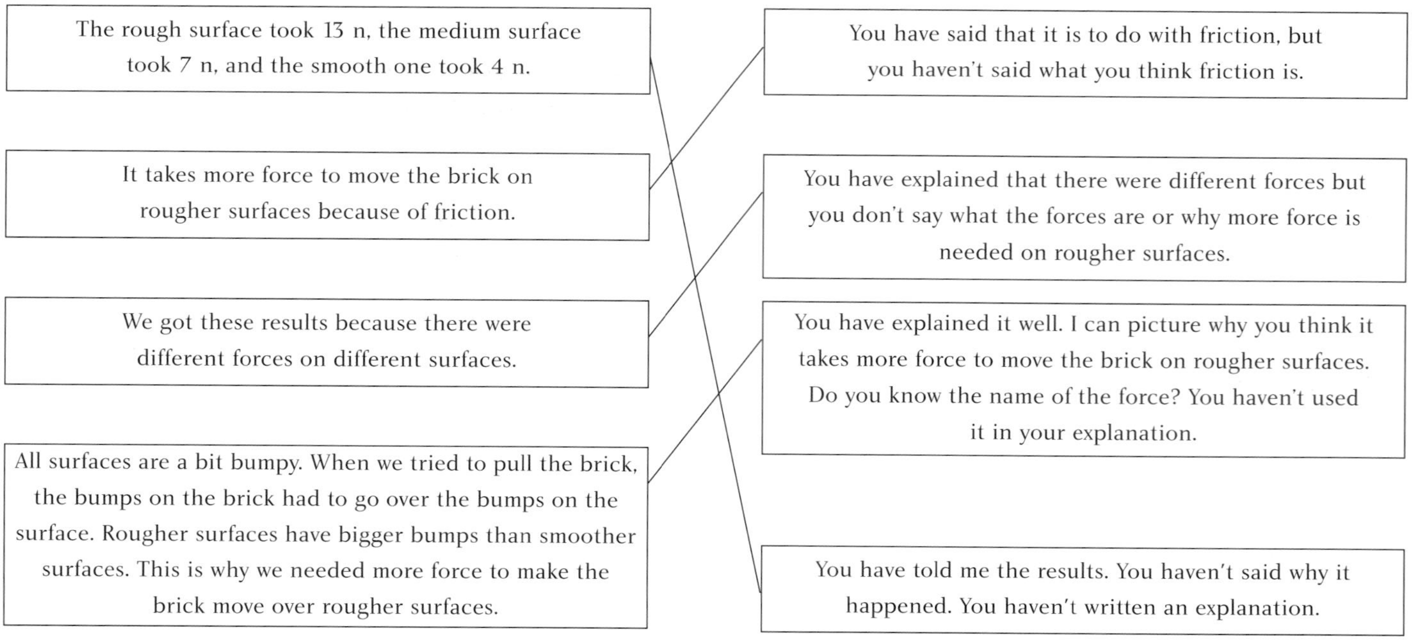

The rough surface took 13 n, the medium surface took 7 n, and the smooth one took 4 n.

It takes more force to move the brick on rougher surfaces because of friction.

We got these results because there were different forces on different surfaces.

All surfaces are a bit bumpy. When we tried to pull the brick, the bumps on the brick had to go over the bumps on the surface. Rougher surfaces have bigger bumps than smoother surfaces. This is why we needed more force to make the brick move over rougher surfaces.

You have said that it is to do with friction, but you haven't said what you think friction is.

You have explained that there were different forces but you don't say what the forces are or why more force is needed on rougher surfaces.

You have explained it well. I can picture why you think it takes more force to move the brick on rougher surfaces. Do you know the name of the force? You haven't used it in your explanation.

You have told me the results. You haven't said why it happened. You haven't written an explanation.

Explaining the evidence

Skill Activity 26

Name .... Date ....

Hakan, Susie, Kelly and Tom investigated different surfaces.
They chose a smooth, a medium and a rough surface.
They found out how much force it took to move a brick over each surface.

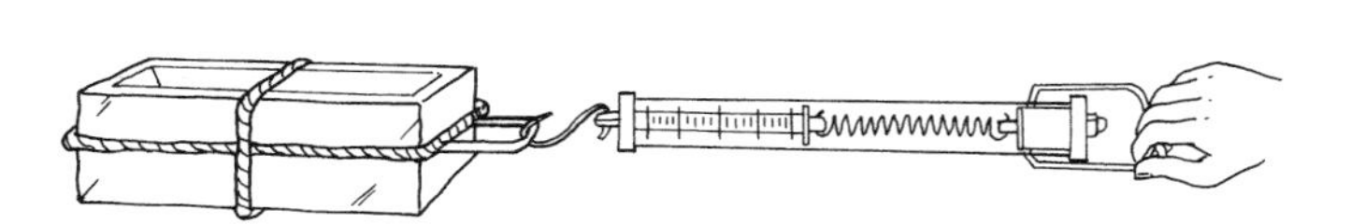

Here are their results.

Type of surface	Force needed to move block in n
smooth	4
medium	7
rough	13

The described their results well. They said "The rougher the surface the more force you need to make the brick move." Their teacher asked them to write a good explanation, and then marked their work. Match each explanation to a comment from their teacher. Draw lines.

Pupils' explanations

The rough surface took 13 n, the medium surface took 7 n, and the smooth one took 4 n.

It takes more force to move the brick on rougher surfaces because of friction.

We got these results because there were different forces on different surfaces.

All surfaces are a bit bumpy. When we tried to pull the brick, the bumps on the brick had to go over the bumps on the surface. Rougher surfaces have bigger bumps than smoother surfaces. This is why we needed more force to make the brick move over rougher surfaces.

Teacher's comments

You have said that it is to do with friction, but you haven't said what you think friction is.

You have explained that there were different forces but you don't say what the forces are or why more force is needed on rougher surfaces.

You have explained it well. I can picture why you think it takes more force to move the brick on rougher surfaces. Do you know the name of the force? You haven't used it in your explanation.

You have told me the results. You haven't said why it happened. You haven't written an explanation.

Evaluating

Evaluating the strength of the evidence is quite a hard skill for children to master. The idea that we want them to understand is that we can never be totally certain of our results so it is important to consider the strength of our evidence. A useful way to think about this is to ask yourself, 'How likely is our conclusion to be true?' and award it a number on a scale of 1 to 10, where 0 = No confidence in my conclusion, and 10 = Total confidence in my conclusion.

Skill Activity 27 introduces lower junior pupils to the idea of evaluating in a simple way by asking them to consider why two groups of pupils got slightly different results although apparently doing very similar scientific enquiries. The idea of evaluating is taken further in the Teaching Scientific Enquiry book for upper junior.

Skill Activity 27

Purpose

To be able to recognise some of the difficulties encountered when carrying out scientific enquiries.

What to do

Ask pupils to read through the first part of the sheet and make sure they understand the context. Get them to pick out all the differences between the two bar charts, while recognising that a similar pattern emerges from both bar charts. Ask pupils to work in pairs to suggest why Group A and Group B did not get the same results. Draw together their responses. They may suggest many different ideas such as:

- Their thermometers weren't measuring exactly the same temperature.
- One group may have used their thermometer incorrectly, e.g. by not putting their eye level with the top of the column of alcohol.
- One group may have used slightly hotter water than the other.
- They may have carried out their enquiry in different parts of the classroom where the temperature was different.
- They may have cut out different sized pieces of material.
- They may have fastened their materials differently.

Evaluating

Skill Activity 27

Name .... *Date* ....

A class investigated what happened when they wrapped different materials round bottles of warm water.
They wanted to know how warm the water would be after 20 minutes.
The pictures show you what they did.

Here are the results from two different groups.

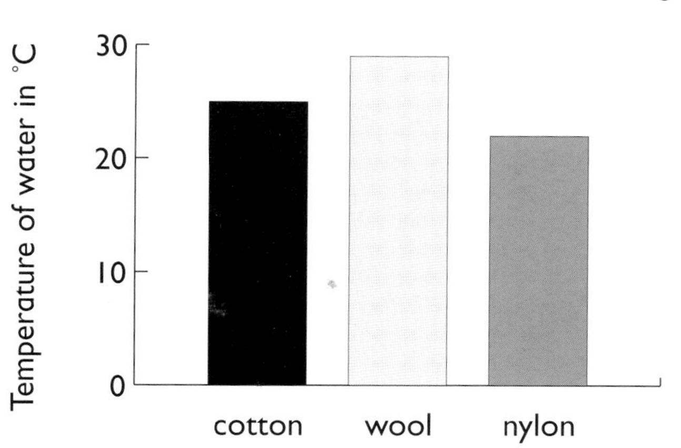

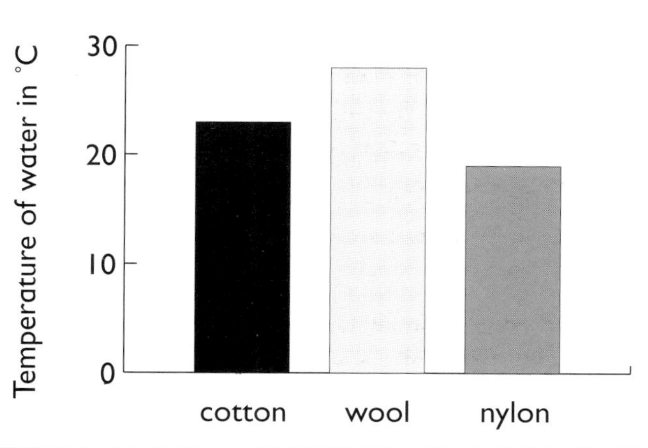

Group A and Group B did not get exactly the same results.
Think of all the reasons why this might be. Write them down.